For all portable keyboards **by Kenneth Baker.**

THE COMPLETE KEYBOARD PL

BOOK 4

G000082275

Wise Publications
London/New York/Sydney/Cologne

4-50

Exclusive Distributors:
Music Sales Limited
8/9 Frith Street, London W1V 5TZ, England
Music Sales Pty. Limited
120 Rothschild Avenue, Rosebery, NSW 2018, Australia

This book © Copyright 1984 by
Wise Publications
UK ISBN 0.7119.1335.8
UK Order No. AM 68552

Music Sales complete catalogue lists thousands of
titles and is free from your local music book shop,
or direct from Music Sales Limited.
Please send £1 in stamps for postage to
Music Sales Limited, 8/9 Frith Street, London W1V 5TZ.

Typeset by Capital Setters Ltd., London
Printed in England by
Halstan & Co. Ltd., Amersham, Bucks.

ABOUT THIS BOOK

In Book Four of The Complete Keyboard
Player you add style to your left hand with
new diminished, augmented, and four-note
minor seventh chords.

You meet new rhythms, in $\frac{6}{8}$ and $\frac{12}{8}$ time, and
you learn about three new keys: A Minor,
G Minor, and E Flat.

Your right hand is as busy as ever with those
effective little fill-ins, chords, and counter
melodies, and at this level of playing the tunes
are even better than usual. They include top
hits in all styles from slow rock to tango.

There are the usual helpful diagrams and
concise text for people teaching themselves,
and keyboard teachers will welcome this new
extension to their favourite keyboard course.

DIMINISHED CHORDS

1 This is a new type of chord, played by your left hand. At the time of writing, diminished chords are not available on keyboards using the "single-finger" chord method. Using the "fingered" chord method, and playing four notes, there are only three diminished chords to learn:-

C° = C Diminished

C♯° = C Sharp Diminished

D° = D Diminished

Each of these three diminished chords has alternative names, depending on which note is to be played in the bass. This does not concern you directly, since your bass notes are being played automatically. However, you should get used to these alternative names as they occur, because you will meet them in other music.

CHORD OF C DIMINISHED (C°, or C^dim)

2

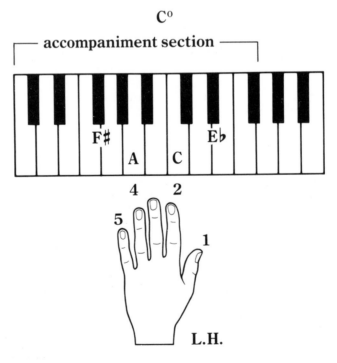

Alternative names (reference only):-

F♯(G♭)°; A°; E♭(D♯)°

You will notice that these alternative names come from the other notes in the chord.

4

SMILE

Words by John Turner & Geoffrey Parsons
Music by Charles Chaplin

Suggested registration: jazz organ + tremolo

Rhythm: bossa nova
Tempo: medium (♩ = 108)

UPSTAIRS DOWNSTAIRS

Composed by Alexander Faris

Suggested registration: French accordion (or brass ensemble)
Arpeggio, if available

Rhythm: waltz
Tempo: quite fast (♩ = 152)

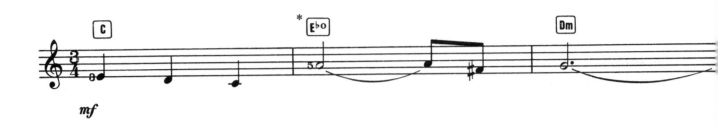

*same as C°

CHORD OF C SHARP (D FLAT) DIMINISHED
(C♯(D♭)°)

3

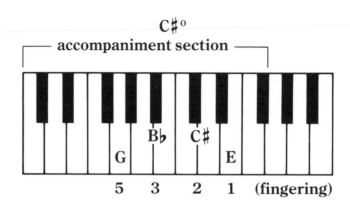

Alternative names (reference only):-

G°; B♭(A♯)°; E°

WHEN YOU WISH UPON A STAR

Words by Ned Washington
Music by Leigh Harline

Suggested registration: string ensemble

Rhythm: swing
Tempo: medium (♩ = 88)

When you wish up - on a star, makes no diff - 'rence
If your heart is in your dream, no re - quest is

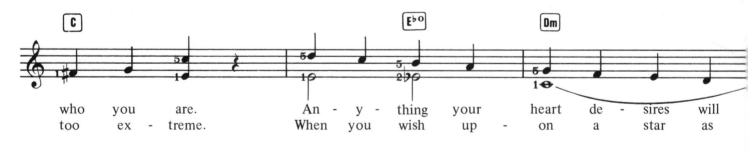

who you are. An - y - thing your heart de - sires will
too ex - treme. When you wish up - on a star as

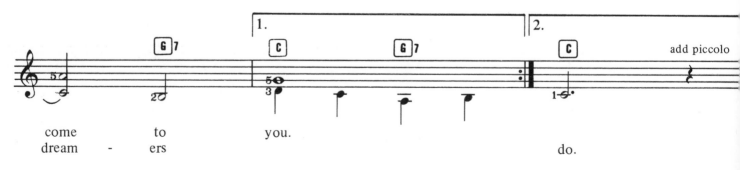

come to you.
dream - ers   do.

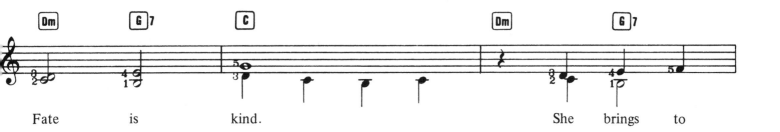

Fate is kind. She brings to

those who love, the sweet ful - fil - ment of their se - cret

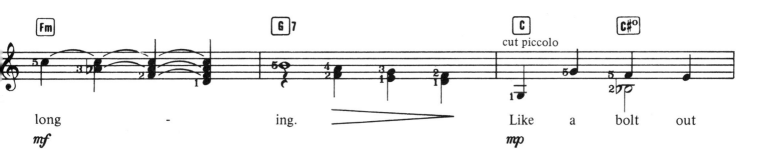

long - ing. Like a bolt out
mf *mp*

of the blue. Fate steps in and sees you through.

When you wish up - on a star, your dream comes true.

AUGMENTED CHORDS

4 This is another new type of chord, played by your left hand ("fingered" method only).

There are only four augmented chords to learn, though, like diminished, each one has ALTERNATIVE NAMES.

CHORD OF C AUGMENTED (C⁺, or Cᵃᵘᵍ)

5

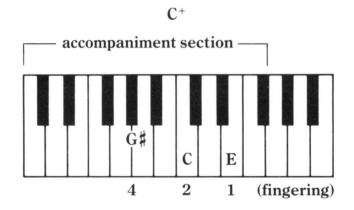

Alternative names:-
G♯(A♭)⁺; E⁺

BALI HA'I

Words by Oscar Hammerstein II
Music by Richard Rodgers
Suggested registration: Hawaiian guitar

Rhythm: beguine, (or bossa nova)
Tempo: medium (♩ = 112)
Synchro-start, if available

Ba - li Ha'i may call you, an - y
Ha'i will whis - per on the

night, an - y day. In your heart _____ you'll hear it
wind of the sea: "Here am I, _____ your spec - ial

call you: "Come a - way, come a - way." Ba - li
is - land! Come to me, come to

*same as C♯°. **Arpeggio. Play the notes of the chord in rapid succession upwards.

10

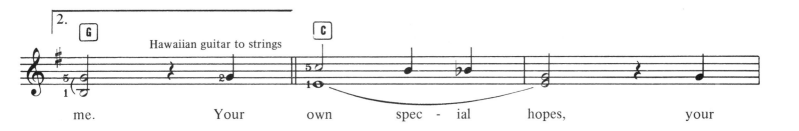

me.   Your   own   spec - ial   hopes,   your

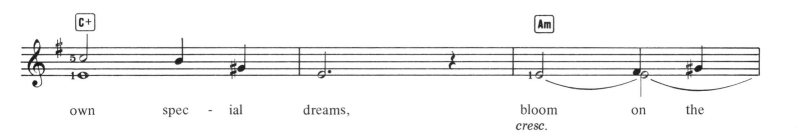

own   spec - ial   dreams,   bloom   on   the
cresc.

hill - side,   and   shine   in   the   streams.   If   you
mf   *mp*

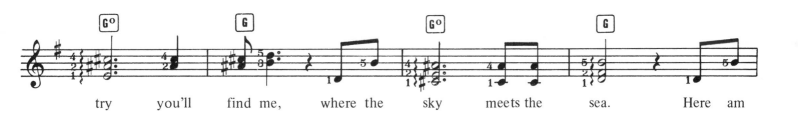

try   you'll   find   me,   where   the   sky   meets   the   sea.   Here   am

I, ___ your   spec - ial   is - land!   Come   to   me,   come   to   me!"   Ba - li

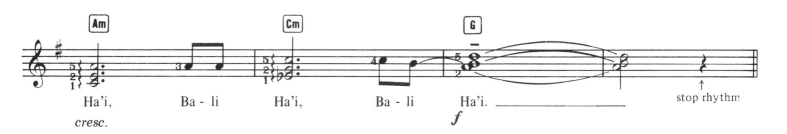

Ha'i,   Ba - li   Ha'i,   Ba - li   Ha'i. ___
cresc.   *f*   stop rhythm

CHORD OF D DIMINISHED (D°)

6

D°

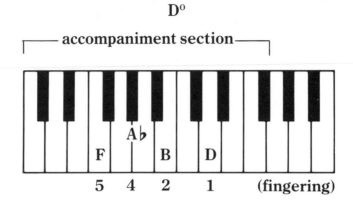

Alternative names:-
F°; A♭(G♯)°; B°

CHORD OF G AUGMENTED (G⁺)

7

G⁺

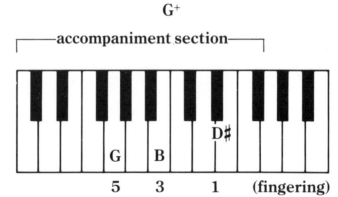

Alternative names:-
B⁺; D♯(E♭)⁺

AIN'T MISBEHAVIN'

Words by Andy Razaf
Music by Thomas Waller & Harry Brooks

Suggested registration: piano (with ½ sustain)
Rhythm: swing
Tempo: medium (♩ = 96)

No-one to talk with,__ all by my-self, no-one to walk with,__ but
I know for cer - tain, __ the one I love. I'm thro' with flirt-in', __ it's

I'm hap-py on the shelf. Ain't mis - be - hav - in', __ I'm sav - in' my love __ for
just you I'm think-in' of Ain't mis - be - hav - in', __ I'm sav - in' my love __ for

you. you.

$\frac{6}{8}$ TIME

8 In this sort of time there are six eighth notes (quavers), or their equivalent, per bar.

In $\frac{6}{8}$ time the dotted quarter note (dotted crotchet): $\downarrow$ is the basic beat, and there are TWO DOTTED QUARTER NOTES per bar:-

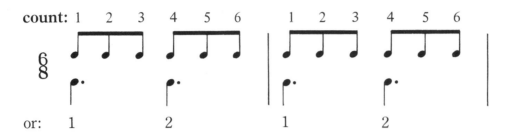

You may count either 6 eighth notes, or 2 dotted quarter notes, whichever is more convenient.

In slow pieces (e.g. *Greensleeves*, p.15), it will probably be more convenient to count 6 in a bar:-

GREENSLEEVES (simplified)

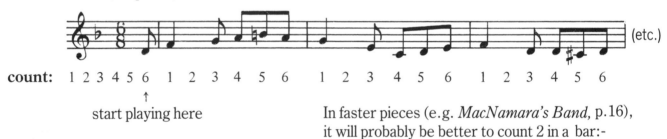

count: 1 2 3 4 5 6   1 2 3 4 5 6   1 2 3 4 5 6   1 2 3 4 5 6   (etc.)

↑
start playing here

In faster pieces (e.g. *MacNamara's Band*, p.16), it will probably be better to count 2 in a bar:-

MacNAMARA'S BAND

count: 1   2   1   2   1   2   1   2

CHORD OF A

9 Using single-finger chord method: play the note "A" in the accompaniment section of your keyboard.

Using fingered chord method:-

A

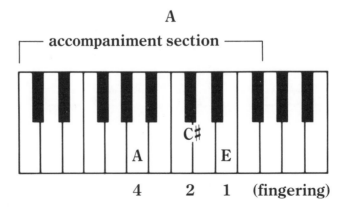

GREENSLEEVES

Traditional

Suggested registration: harpsichord (with ½ sustain)

Rhythm: off, or waltz (♩ = ♩)
Tempo: medium (♩ = 120)

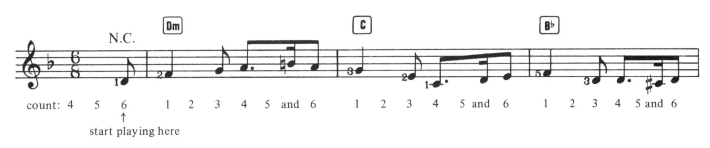

count: 4 5 6   1 2 3 4 5 and 6   1 2 3 4 5 and 6   1 2 3 4 5 and 6

↑
start playing here

p

1 2 3 4 5 6   1 2 3 4 5 and 6   1 2 3 4 5 and 6

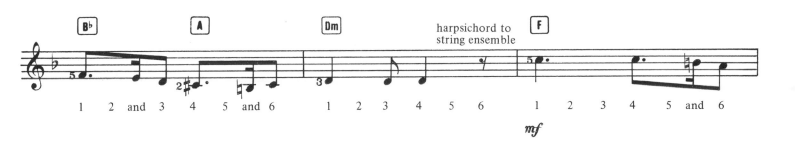

harpsichord to
string ensemble

1 2 and 3 4 5 and 6   1 2 3 4 5 6   1 2 3 4 5 and 6

mf

1 2 3 4 5 and 6   1 2 3 4 5 and 6   1 2 3 4 5 6

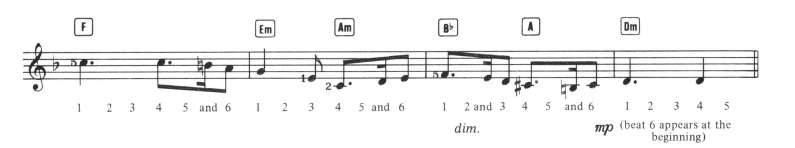

1 2 3 4 5 and 6   1 2 3 4 5 and 6   1 2 and 3 4 5 and 6   1 2 3 4 5

dim.   *mp* (beat 6 appears at the beginning)

MacNAMARA'S BAND

Words by John J. Stamford
Music by Shamus O'Connor

Suggested registration: brass ensemble

Rhythm: march 6/8
Tempo: medium (♪. = 116)
Synchro-start, if available

VERSE

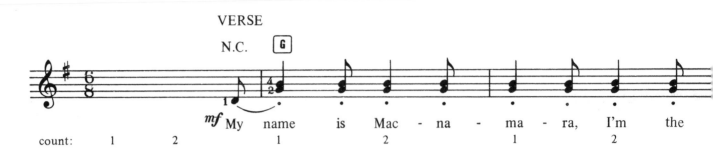

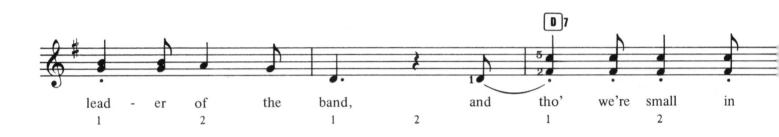

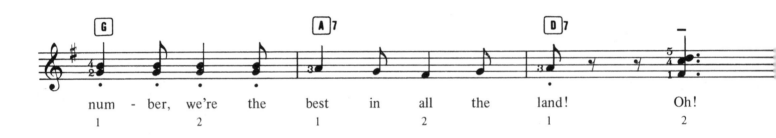

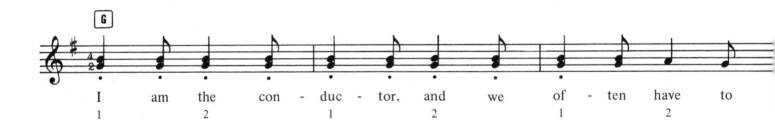

CHORUS

add piccolo

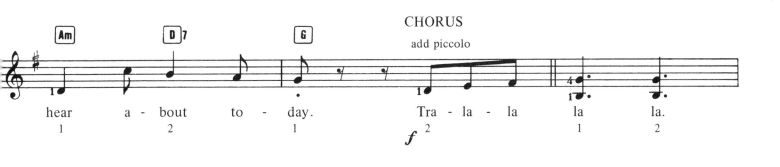

hear a - bout to - day. Tra - la - la la la.

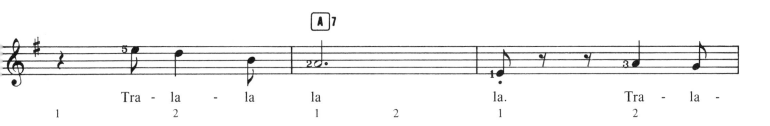

Tra - la - la la la. Tra - la -

la la la la la la la la la.

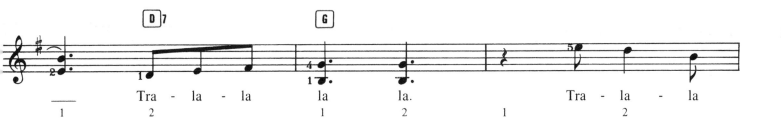

Tra - la - la la la. Tra - la - la

la la. Tra - la - la la la la

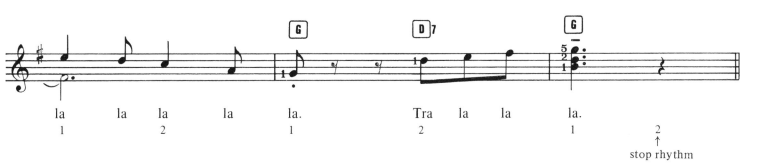

la la la la la. Tra la la la.

stop rhythm

$\frac{12}{8}$ TIME

10

In this sort of time there are twelve eighth notes (quavers), or their equivalent, per bar.

In $\frac{12}{8}$ time the dotted quarter note (dotted crotchet): ♩. is the basic beat, and there are FOUR DOTTED QUARTER NOTES per bar:-

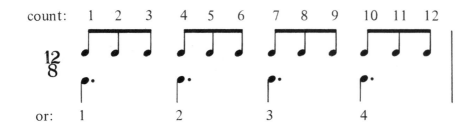

In most $\frac{12}{8}$ tunes (like *House Of The Rising Sun,* on this page), it will probably be best to start by counting the full 12 in a bar, switching to 4 in a bar later, when you are quite sure of the tune:-

HOUSE OF THE RISING SUN

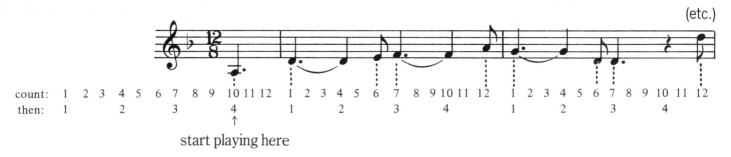

start playing here

HOUSE OF THE RISING SUN

Traditional

Suggested registration: *jazz organ, with chorus*

Rhythm: slow rock
Tempo: slow (♩. = 66)
Synchro-start, if available

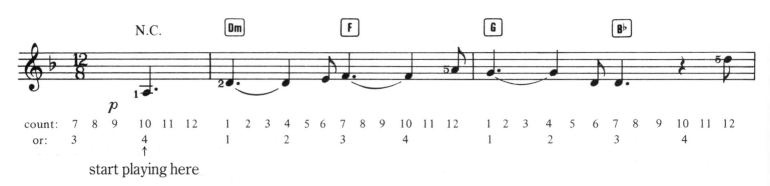

start playing here

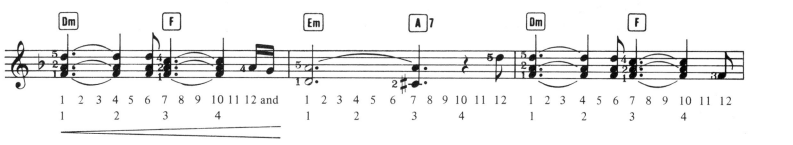

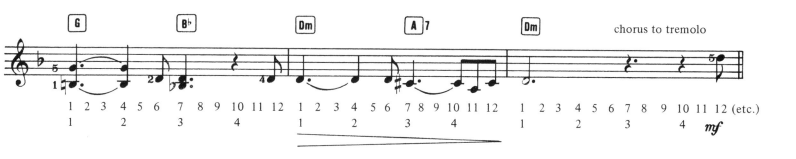

chorus to tremolo

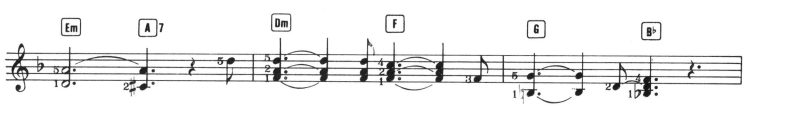

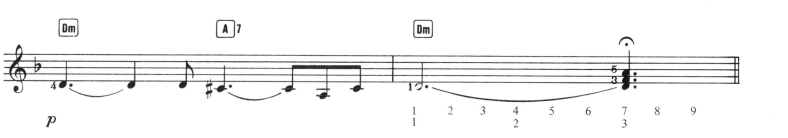

MEMORY

Music by Andrew Lloyd Webber
Text by Trevor Nunn after T.S. Eliot

Suggested registration: organ, with tremolo
Arpeggio, if available

Rhythm: slow rock
Tempo: slow (♪. = 66)

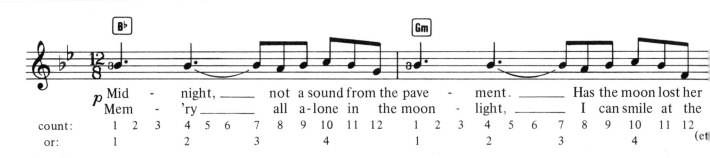

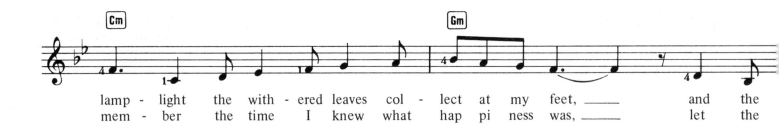

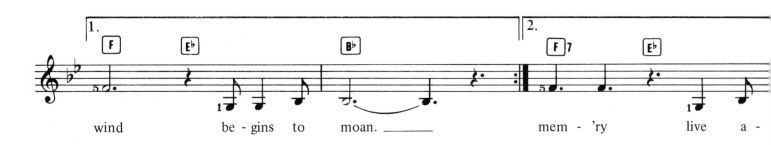

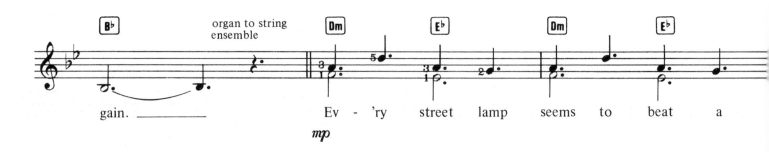

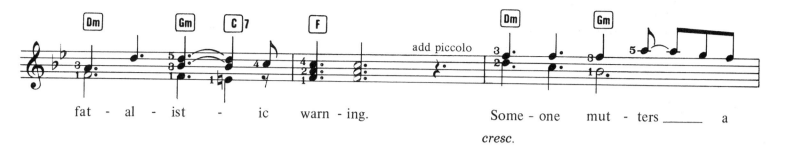

fat - al - ist - ic warn - ing. Some - one mut - ters _____ a

cresc.

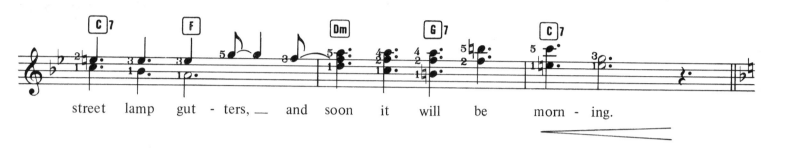

street lamp gut - ters, _ and soon it will be morn - ing.

Touch me, _ it's so ea - sy to leave me _ all a-lone with the mem - 'ry _ of my days in the

f

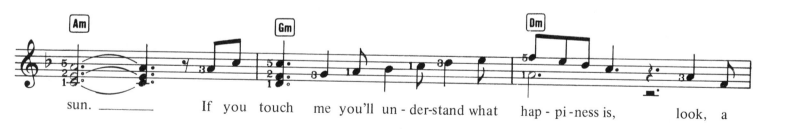

sun. _____ If you touch me you'll un - der-stand what hap - pi - ness is, look, a

new day has be - gun. _____ 1 2 3 4

dim.

mp

stop rhythm

MINOR SEVENTH CHORDS

11 These are variations of "minor" chords, played by your left hand.

CHORD OF A MINOR SEVENTH (Am7)

12 Using single-finger chord method:-

1. Play single note "A", together with any black note to its left PLUS any white note to its left.

Using fingered chord method:-

or:

2*. Play single note "A", together with ANY THREE NOTES to its right.

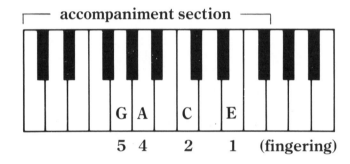

Am7

CHORD OF D MINOR SEVENTH (Dm7)

13 Using single-finger chord method:-

1. Play single note "D", together with any black note to its left PLUS any white note to its left.

Using fingered chord method:-

or:

2*. Play single note "D", together with ANY THREE NOTES to its right.

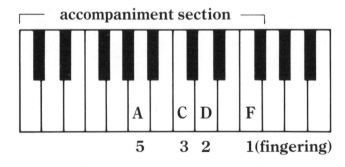

Dm7

*Depending on make and model.

THE WONDER OF YOU

Words & Music by Baker Knight

Suggested registration: *jazz flute or rock guitar*

Rhythm: swing
Tempo: quite slow (♩ = 80)

When no-one else can un-der-stand me, ___ when ev-'ry-thing I do is

p

wrong. You give me love and con-so-la-tion, ___

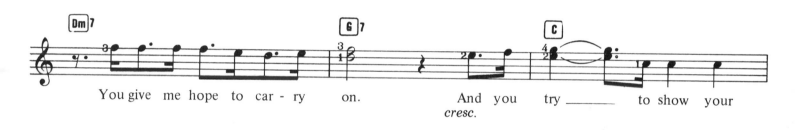

You give me hope to car-ry on. And you try ___ to show your

cresc.

love ___ for me in ev-'ry-thing you do. ___ That's the

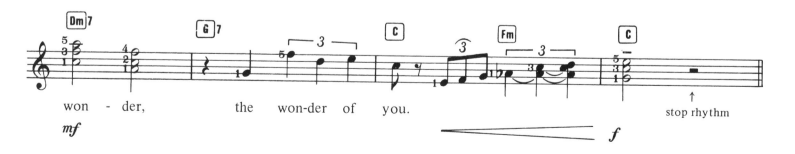

won-der, the won-der of you.

mf

stop rhythm

f

CHORD OF G MINOR SEVENTH (Gm7)

14 Using single-finger chord method:-

Locate "G" in the accompaniment section of your keyboard. Convert this into "Gm7" (see this book, p.22, and your owner's manual).

Using fingered chord method:-

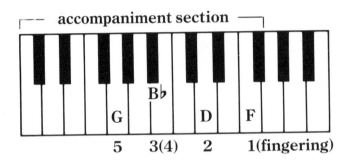

Gm7

GREEN EYES

Words by L. Wolfe Gilbert & Reg Connelly
Music by Nilo Menendez

Suggested registration: accordion

Rhythm: rhumba
Tempo: medium (♩ = 116)
Synchro-start, if available

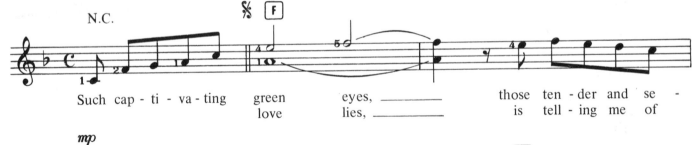

Such cap - ti - va - ting green eyes, _____ those ten - der and se -
love lies, _____ is tell - ing me of

rene eyes, _____ those fas - cin - at - ing green eyes, _____
love ties, _____ I look in - to your green eyes, _____

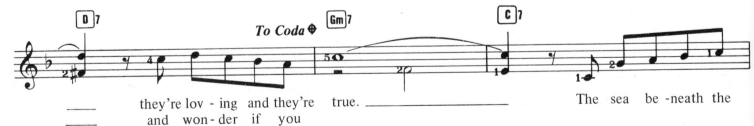

_____ they're lov - ing and they're true. _____ The sea be -neath the
_____ and won - der if you

blue   skies, _____ is en - vy - ing your green   eyes, _____

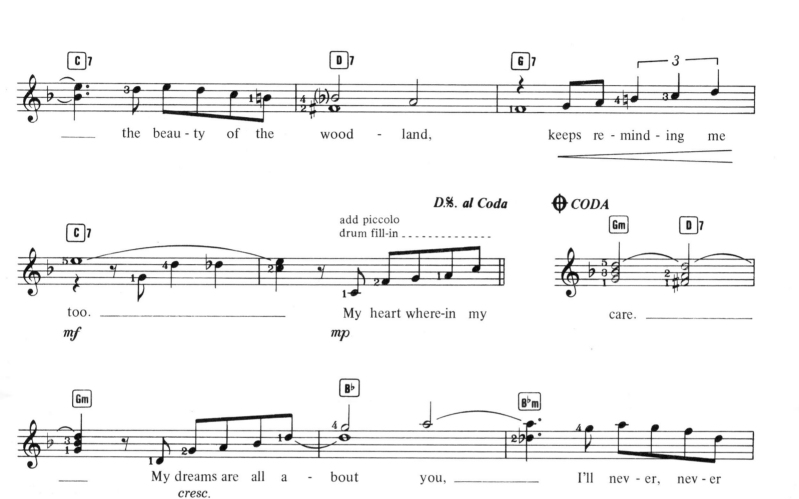

_____ the beau - ty of the wood - land,   keeps re - mind - ing me

D.%. al Coda   ⊕ *CODA*

add piccolo
drum fill-in

too. _____   My heart where-in my   care. _____

mf   *mp*

My dreams are all a - bout   you, _____   I'll nev - er, nev - er

cresc.

doubt   you, _____   one look in - to your green   eyes and

I   find my hea - ven   there.

f

stop rhythm

ON THE SUNNY SIDE OF THE STREET

Words by Dorothy Fields
Music by Jimmy McHugh

Suggested registration: *jazz organ, with tremolo*

Rhythm: swing
Tempo: medium (♩ = 116)
Synchro-start, if available

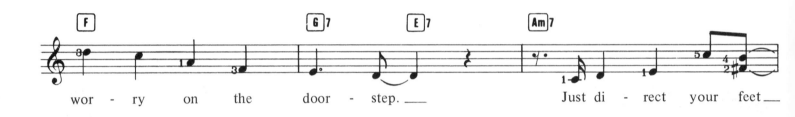

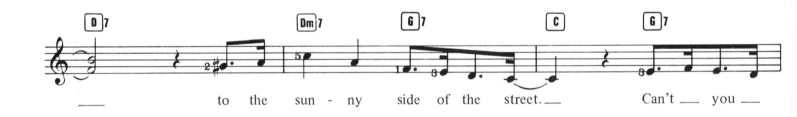

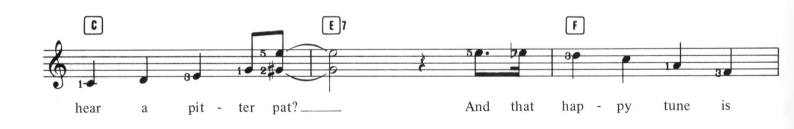

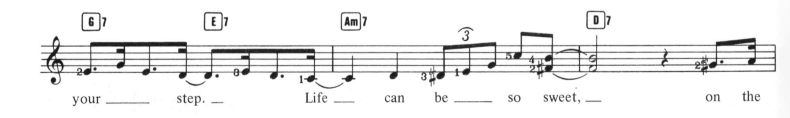

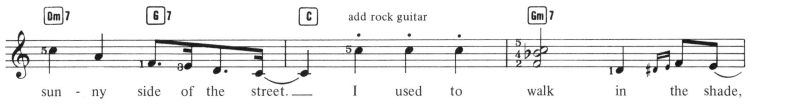

sun - ny side of the street. ___ I used to walk in the shade,

___ with those blues ___ on par - ade. ___ But

I'm not a - fraid, ___ this ___ ro - ver crossed ___

o - ver. If I nev - er ___ have ___ a cent, ___ I'll be

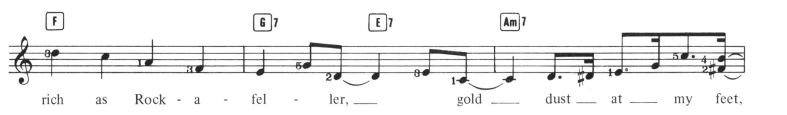

rich as Rock - a - fel - ler, ___ gold ___ dust ___ at ___ my feet,

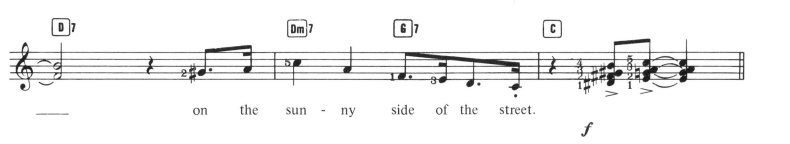

___ on the sun - ny side of the street.

CHORD OF E MINOR SEVENTH (Em7)

15

Using single-finger chord method:-

Locate "E" in the accompaniment section of your keyboard. Convert this into "Em7" (see this book, p.22, and your owner's manual).

Using fingered chord method:-

Em7

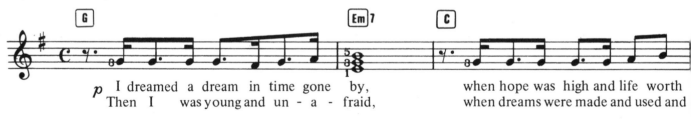

I DREAMED A DREAM

Music by Claude-Michel Schonberg
Lyric by Herbert Kretzmer
Original Text by Alain Boublil & Jean-Marc Natel

Suggested registration: string ensemble

Rhythm: rock
Tempo: quite slow (♩ = 80)

night.   With their voi - ces soft as thun - der. ____

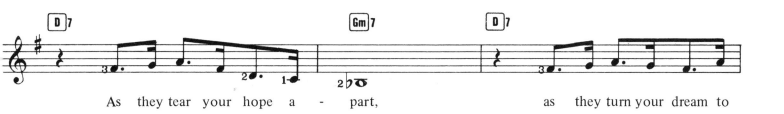

As they tear your hope a - part,   as they turn your dream to

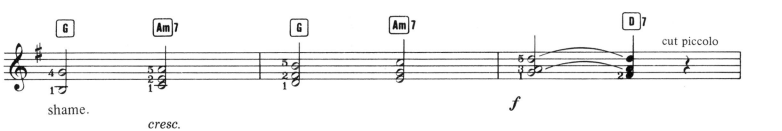

shame.   *cresc.*   *f*   cut piccolo

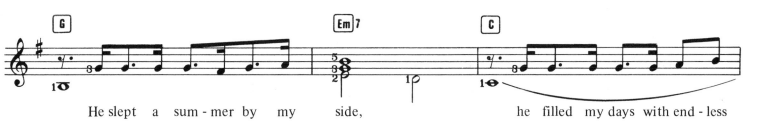

He slept a sum - mer by my side,   he filled my days with end - less

won - der. ____   He took my child - hood in his stride,

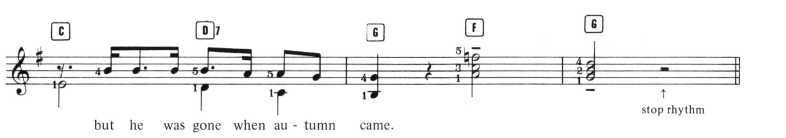

but he was gone when au - tumn came.   stop rhythm

CHORD OF D   *Lollipops and Roses*

16 Using single-finger chord method:-

Play "D" (the higher one) in the accompaniment section of your keyboard.

Using fingered chord method:-

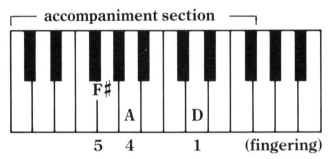

D

CHORD OF E FLAT MINOR SEVENTH (E♭m7)

17 Using single-finger chord method:-

Locate "E♭" (the higher one) in the accompaniment section of your keyboard.

Using fingered chord method:-

Convert this into E♭m7 (see this book, p.22, and your owner's manual).

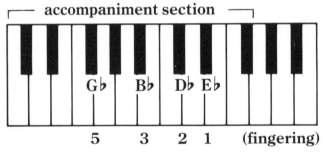

E♭m7

CHORD OF A FLAT SEVENTH (A♭7)

18 Using single-finger chord method:-

Locate "A♭" in the accompaniment section of your keyboard. Convert this into A♭7 (see

Book One, p.42ff., and your owner's manual).

Using fingered chord method:-

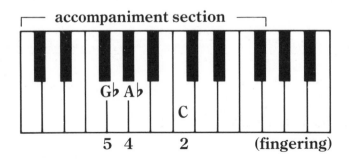

A♭7

CHORD OF D FLAT (D♭)

19 Using single-finger chord method:-

Play "D♭" (the higher one) in the accompaniment section of your keyboard.

Using fingered chord method:-

D♭

accompaniment section

A♭ D♭ F

4   2   1 (fingering)

KEY OF A MINOR *Feelings*

20 The key of A Minor is related to the key of C Major. Neither key requires any black notes:-

scale/key of A Minor

A B C D E F G A

scale/key of C (Major)

C D E F G A B C

Feelings (p.34) begins in the key of A Minor, and finishes in the key of C.

KEY OF G MINOR *La Cumparsita*

21 The key of G Minor is related to the key of B♭ Major. Two flats (B Flat, and E Flat) are required to make up their scales:-

scale/key of G Minor

G A (B♭) C D (E♭) F G

scale/key of B♭ (Major)

(B♭) C D (E♭) F G A (B♭)

La Cumparsita (p.36) is in the key of G Minor throughout.

LOLLIPOPS AND ROSES

Words & Music by Tony Velona

Suggested registration: pipe organ, with tremolo

Rhythm: waltz
Tempo: medium (♩ = 92)

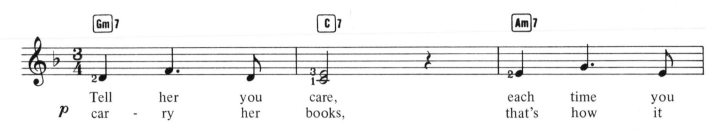

Tell her you care,   each time you
car - ry her books,   that's how it

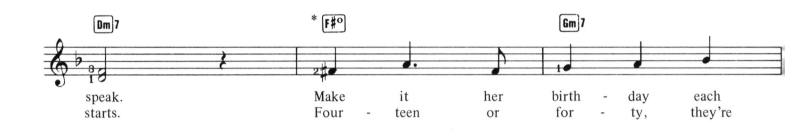

speak.   Make it her birth - day each
starts.   Four - teen or for - ty, they're

day of the week.   Bring her
kids in their hearts.   Keep them

mf

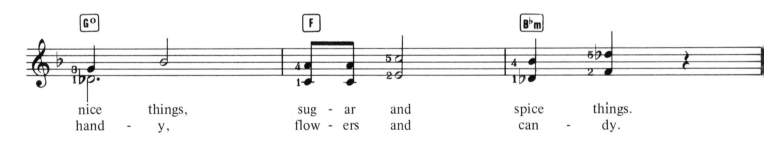

nice things,   sug - ar and   spice things.
hand - y,   flow - ers and   can - dy.

To Coda ⊕

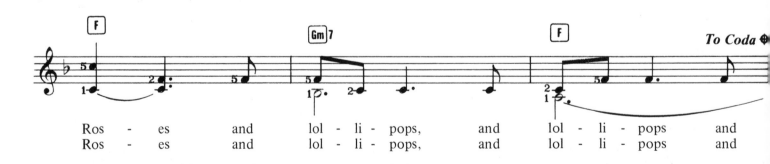

Ros - es and lol - li - pops, and lol - li - pops and
Ros - es and lol - li - pops, and lol - li - pops and

* Same as C°

FEELINGS (DIME)

Spanish Lyrics by Thomas Fundora
Music & English Words by Morris Albert

Suggested registration: bright piano (with tremolo)

Rhythm: bossa nova
Tempo: medium (♩ = 100)

you'll nev-er come a - gain.

Feel - ings, wo wo wo, feel - ings, ___

___ wo wo wo feel you ___ a - gain in my

To Coda ⊕

strings to piano

arms. ___ Feel - ings, ___

mp

feel - ings like I nev - er lost you ___ and feel-ings like I'll

D.%. al Coda ⊕ *CODA*

nev - er have ___ you a - gain in my arms. ___

stop rhythm

LA CUMPARSITA

By Rodriguez

Suggested registration: French accordion

Rhythm: tango
Tempo: fairly fast (♩ = 120)

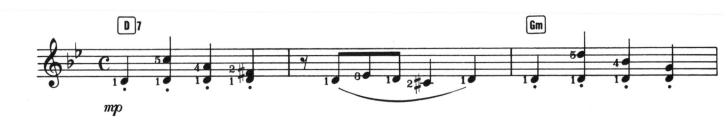

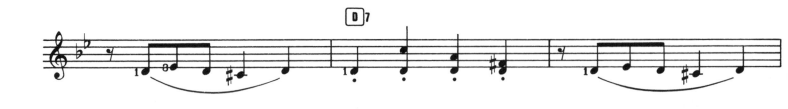

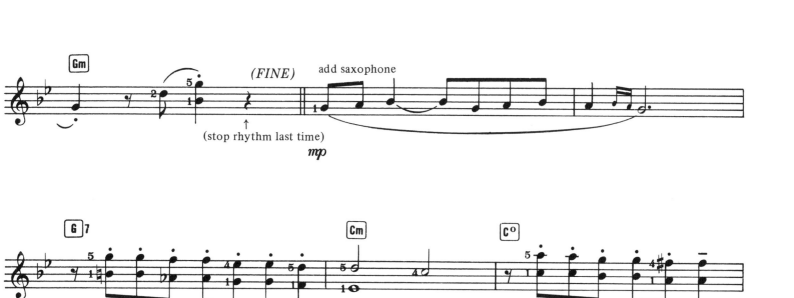

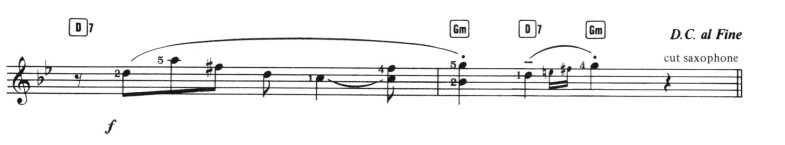

KEY OF E FLAT AND KEY OF C MINOR

22 These two keys are related, since both their scales require three flats: B Flat, E Flat, and A Flat:-

scale/key of E♭ (Major)

Ⓔ♭ F G Ⓐ♭ Ⓑ♭ C D Ⓔ♭

scale/key of C Minor

C D Ⓔ♭ F G Ⓐ♭ Ⓑ♭ C

Watch out for these three flats in:-

Lady In Red, p.39 (key of E♭)
Sunrise Sunset, p.42 (key of C Minor)
El Cumbanchero, p.44 (key of C Minor)

CHORD OF B FLAT SEVENTH (B♭7)

23 Using single-finger chord method:-

Locate "B♭" in the accompaniment section of your keyboard. Convert this note into "B♭7" (see Book One, p.42ff., and your owner's manual).

Using fingered chord method:-

B♭7

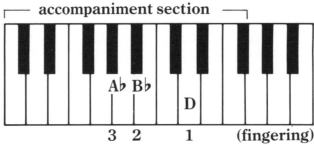

CHORD OF A FLAT (A♭)

24 Using single-finger chord method:-

Play "A♭" in the accompaniment section of your keyboard.

Using fingered chord method:-

A♭

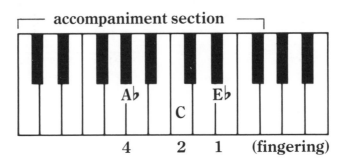

THE LADY IN RED

Words & Music by Chris De Burgh

Suggested registration: jazz organ, with chorus (chorale)

Rhythm: rock
Tempo: quite fast (♩ = 76)
Synchro-start, if available

VERSE
N.C.

I've nev-er seen you look-ing so love-ly as you did ___ to-night,___
nev-er seen so man-y men ask ___ you if you want-ed to dance,___

___ I've nev-er seen you shine so bright.
___ they're look-ing for a little ro - mance.

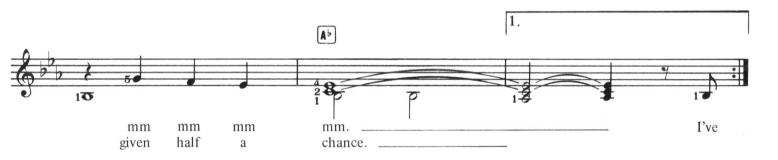

1.

mm mm mm mm. _____ I've
given half a chance. _____

2.

___ And I have nev-er seen that dress you're wear - ing, or the

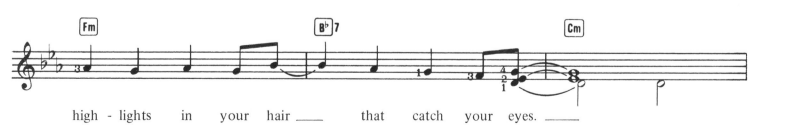

high - lights in your hair ___ that catch your eyes. ___

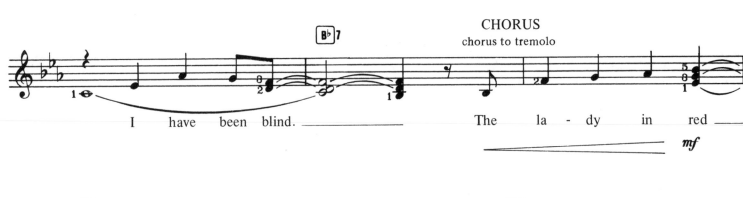

CHORUS
chorus to tremolo

I have been blind. _____ The la - dy in red _____

mf

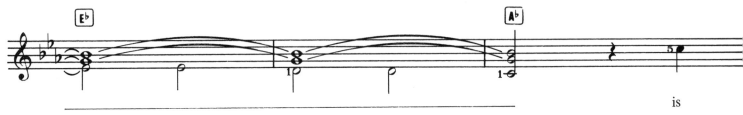

is

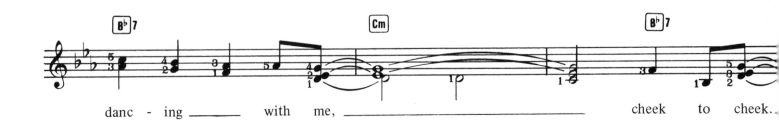

danc - ing _____ with me, _____ cheek to cheek.

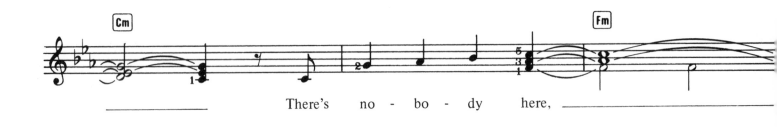

There's no - bo - dy here, _____

it's just you and me, _____

it's where I wan - na be. _____ But

I hard - ly know _____

this beau - ty by my side. _____

cresc.

_____ I'll nev - er for - get _____

f

_____ the

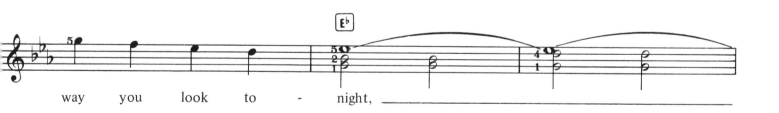

way you look to - night, _____

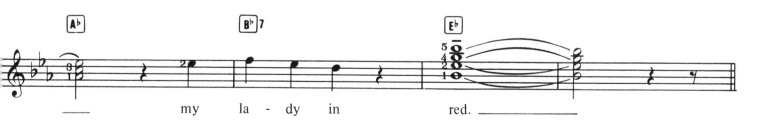

_____ my la - dy in red. _____

SUNRISE, SUNSET

Words by Sheldon Harnick
Music by Jerry Bock

Suggested registration: French accordion

Rhythm: waltz
Tempo: fast (♩ = 168)

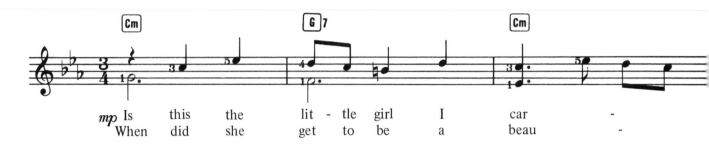

mp Is this the lit - tle girl I car -
When did she get to be a beau -

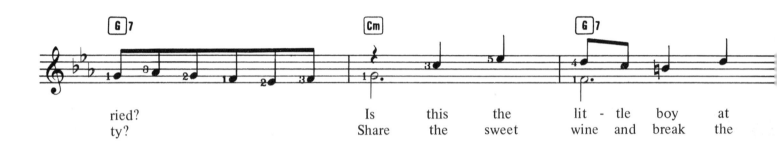

ried? Is this the lit - tle boy at
ty? Share the sweet wine and break the

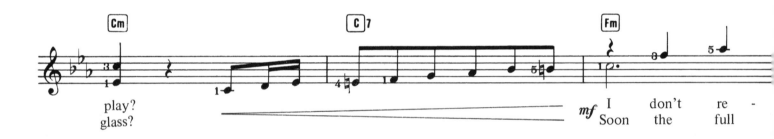

play? mf I don't re -
glass? Soon the full

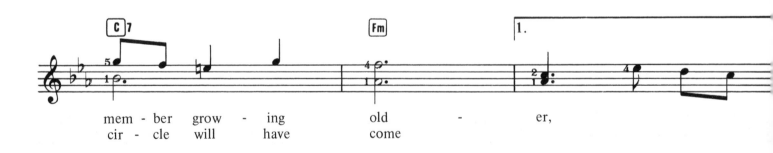

mem - ber grow - ing old - er,
cir - cle will have come

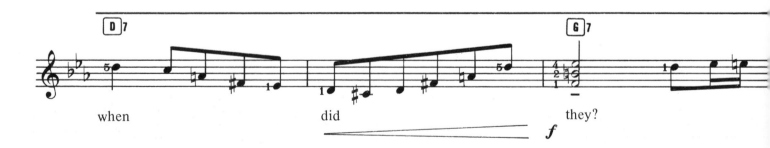

when did they? f

to   pass.

Sun - rise,   sun - set,

sun - rise   sun - set,   swift - ly   flow the

days.   Seed - lings turn

o - ver - night   to   sun   -   flow'rs

blos - som - ing   e - ven   as   we   gaze.   stop rhythm

EL CUMBANCHERO

English Lyric by Joe Crayhorn & George Williams
Music by Rafael Hernandez

Suggested registration: *jazz organ, with tremolo*

Rhythm: samba
Tempo: fast (♩ = 132)
Synchro-start, if available

El cum - ba, cum - ba,   cum - ba, cum - ban - che - ro.
cum - ba, cum - ba,   cum - ba, cum - ban - che - ro.
cum - ba, cum - ba,   cum - ba, cum - ban - che - ro.

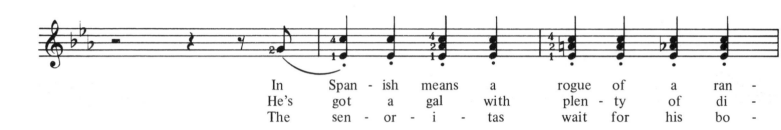

In   Span - ish   means   a   rogue   of   a   ran -
He's   got   a   gal   with   plen - ty   of   di -
The   sen - or - i - tas   wait   for   his   bo -

che - ro.   While   the   oth - er   gau - chos
ne - ro.   He   will   tell   her she's   the
le - ro.   But   El   Cum - ban - che - ro

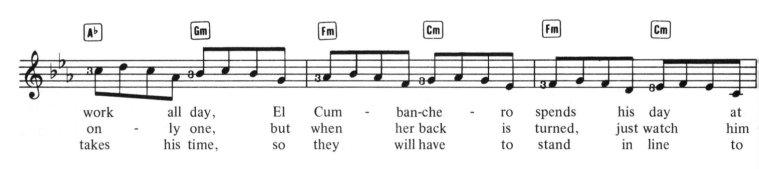

work   all   day,   El   Cum - ban-che - ro   spends   his   day   at
on - ly   one,   but   when   her back   is   turned,   just watch   him
takes   his   time,   so   they   will have   to   stand   in   line   to

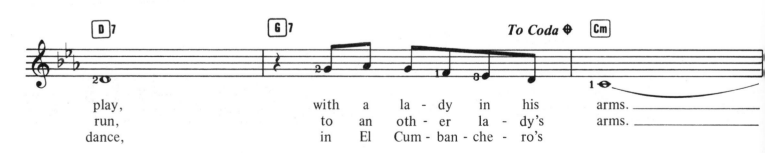

To Coda ⊕

play,   with   a   la - dy   in   his   arms. _____
run,   to   an   oth - er   la - dy's   arms. _____
dance,   in   El   Cum - ban - che - ro's

CHORD CHART (Showing all "fingered chords" used in the course)

C
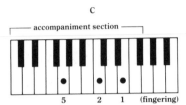

D♭
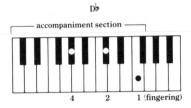

D
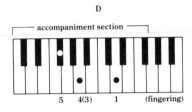

Cm
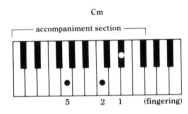

C#(D♭)°
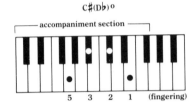

Dm
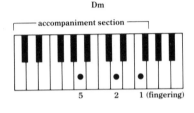

C7
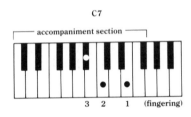

Dm7
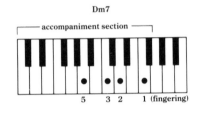

C°
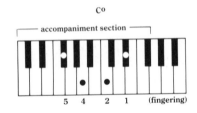

D7
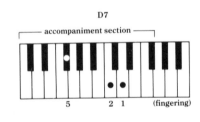

C+
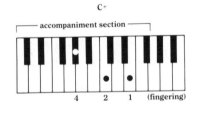

D°
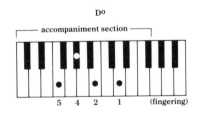

E♭

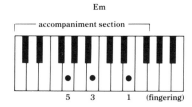

Em

F

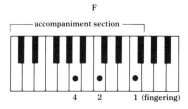

E♭m7

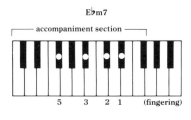

Em7

Fm

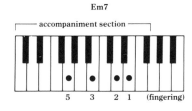
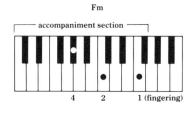

E♭°

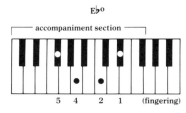

E7

F7

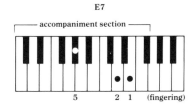
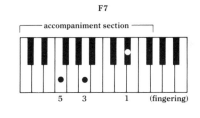

F°

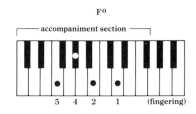

F♯°

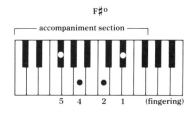

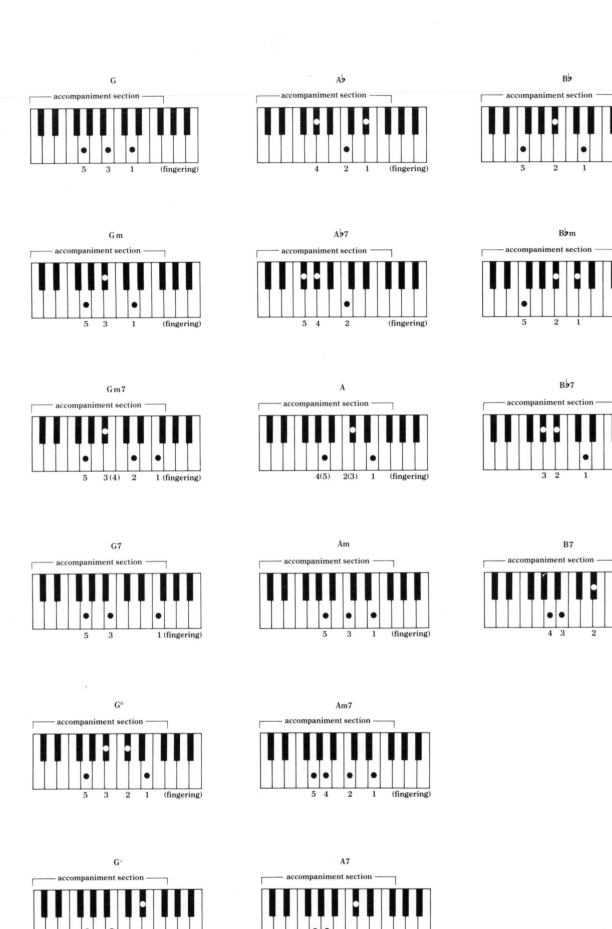